"The gift of humor is surely a grace to get you through!"

Mari Bindas

no lumps,
thank you.
~a bra anthologie.

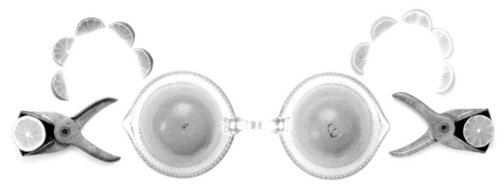

uplifting stories of breast cancer survival.

Schiffer Books are available at special discounts for bulk purchases for sales promotions or premiums. Special editions, including personalized covers, corporate imprints, and excerpts can be created in large quantities for special needs. For more information contact the publisher:

Published by Schiffer Publishing Ltd.
4880 Lower Valley Road
Atglen, PA 19310
Phone: (610) 593-1777; Fax: (610) 593-2002
E-mail: Info@schifferbooks.com

For the largest selection of fine reference books on this and related subjects, please visit our website at
www.schifferbooks.com

We are always looking for people to write books on new and related subjects. If you have an idea for a book, please contact us at proposals@schifferbooks.com

In Europe, Schiffer books are distributed by
Bushwood Books
6 Marksbury Ave.
Kew Gardens
Surrey TW9 4JF England
Phone: 44 (0) 20 8392 8585;
Fax: 44 (0) 20 8392 9876
E-mail: info@bushwoodbooks.co.uk
Website: www.bushwoodbooks.co.uk

Dedication.

To breast cancer survivors everywhere, who show us there is healing in laughter.

this bra's for you.

It was 1974-ish. I was a teenager, sitting at the dinner table with my two older brothers and mother. My father joined us after mowing the lawn, wearing a white tank undershirt. Mom quickly whipped off her blouse and sat there confidently in her bra, saying, "If he can show up for dinner in his underwear...so can I." Dad went and got a shirt.

That was my mother, Dorothy: always stretching boundaries, living and loving with humor, and speaking her mind.

She was a designer for Hollywood Vassarette Lingerie in Minneapolis in the 1950s when she met my father. I remember her telling my sewing class in high school that fashion design isn't all glamour, and talking about properly fitting underwear. But, as she showed us photographs of her flowing nightgowns and lacy robes on lovely models, I thought it looked pretty glamorous and wondered why she gave it up for us.

Several years ago, the Hotel Donaldson, an upscale, boutique hotel designed around regional artists' work, began sponsoring a breast cancer benefit called "Bras on Broadway." They put out a call for local artists to create wonderful, wearable art bras for the auction to benefit local women dealing with breast cancer. How fun could that be! My first art bra, a wearable "Breast Nest," was a curvy, woven combination of copper wire, grasses, and fibers. It even came with a little bird that I dug out of our old Christmas ornaments, to sit on a finger. I was so excited to share it with Mom, and we delighted in the amazing creativity of so many artists at the big event. We always talked about designing some fun art bras together. We never got around to that.

As a fine art photographer—objects, including bird nests, sea shells, and metal pieces I discovered on the street—were always creeping into my work. Soon I began to create found object art bras in my own style, piecing things together and combining parts. Mom, an accomplished painter, was my biggest fan, tossing around ideas over margaritas on the deck. Her sense of humor and creative spirit still inspires me, even after losing her three years ago.

So, this book is for you, Mom. I miss you so much and I'm so happy to be designing bras all these years after you did the same. And you were right. Designing isn't glamorous at all... but it's pretty fun.

~ Meg Spielman Peldo

just to smile.

Growing up as a child of the 60s & 70s, there was talk of bras everywhere. There were women on the news burning them...there were adults whispering about teenage girls bouncing around without them...and warnings that we would end up looking like those women in National Geographic if we didn't wear one! As girls, we were so excited to finally get our first bra...only to toss them aside just a few years later! There was the old test...put a vertical pencil (eraser side up) under your breast and if it doesn't fall out, well, you better get a bra on, because you're starting to sag! There were the funny slang terms going around the schoolyard, there were chuckles in fumbling with hooks and straps, and snapping them like rubber bands in the locker room.

There is a universal vibe of humor surrounding these garments that "lift and separate" our breasts. It crosses gender, age, and culture. It's good medicine for all of us to let down our guard and laugh, but it's especially good for those mothers, daughters, sisters, and friends who are fighting breast cancer and transitioning into a new relationship with their breasts, or for those who have won the battle and are moving on. My hope is to bring a smile to your spirit and a chuckle to your heart with this book, by sharing my interpretations of the silly terms that are associated with bras & breasts.

Bra-vo to that funny invention designed to hold our melons...knockers...or rack.

~ Meg Spielman Peldo

just to share.

All of us in the cancer field realize a great sense of purpose and meaning behind what we do. This meaning comes from the amazing insight, strength, and humor we are able to witness as people become extraordinary cancer survivors. We are able to see people—against all odds—rise above their situation: teachers who inspire schools of people, community members rallying to raise money for the cause, and families and friends uniting to help people through the bad moments. We are able to see people move forward, forever changed, with a renewed sense of purpose. Through work with the embrace Cancer Survivorship Program, I realize how survivors often provide the most meaningful and practical advice and hope to each other.

As frightening as a breast cancer diagnosis is, there are "light" moments that give us hope and rejuvenation during challenging times. There are moments along the journey when you simply have to laugh out loud. Surprisingly enough, laughter can often be heard throughout cancer centers. There are times humor can be the one thing that gets a person through the difficult treatments, the changes in their bodies, and the fear of the unknown. My hope is that as you read this, you feel the kinship that is part of this community of survivorship.

When I first saw Meg's art bras at Bras on Broadway three years ago, I immediately loved them. They were funny, fresh, and light-hearted. Afterward, I met her and she told me about her idea for a bra art book. I knew this could be the perfect medium to incorporate what we hear and learn everyday from the cancer survivors so that others, too, could be blessed with their insights. I was honored to meet Kim Wagner when she spoke at a survivorship fundraiser and reunited with her as she started traveling the journey as a breast cancer survivor. Kim's ability to connect with others and bring out those insights is remarkable! Thank you to Kim and the many wonderful contributors to the book. You will continue to inspire us, the people you meet, and each person who reads this book.

~ Dr. Shelby Terstriep

just for hope.

The women who shared their stories in this book have much in common. Breast cancer changes the life of the recipient as well as the lives of her family and friends. This was the universal thread in every story submitted.

I spoke to many women. Some experienced radical surgical procedures followed by months of treatment. Others underwent a lumpectomy with no further treatment required. Whatever the scenario, the truth is cancer changes how one looks at life.

I heard the same conclusion again and again: life is unrelentingly unpredictable.

As breast cancer survivors, we have had the opportunity to look at life from a different perspective and, for the most part, we are grateful. We will never again look at a sunset, flower, baby, or the love of a significant other in the same manner.

We all share the common hope that we are—or will be—at the conclusion of the journey, cancer-free. The fact is, despite incredible medical advances in the field of oncology, some of us will die from breast cancer. Let this bit of an anthologie make it clearly evident: we all did our best to live. Really live.

~ Kim Wagner

FIGHTERS

I am a 28-year survivor. ~ Cari Wefel

Today's "Cancer Survivors" are receiving the benefits of yesterday's research. I hope my cancer journey will be of value to someone in the future. My cancer journey is still in progress and will be until the day I die. ~ Joyce Ertelt

I learned most of us are much stronger than we ever believed possible. We can go through life or grow through life. Each person has a choice. ~ Marietta Weber

knockers.

(vintage boxing gloves, elastic bandage wrap, daisies, Band-Aids & painted rocks)

DIAGNOSIS

When I was diagnosed with breast cancer and we had to tell the kids, they could tell that we had important news. My seven year-old daughter asked if I was pregnant. I told her this was the one time that I wished I was pregnant! ~ Teri Gorze

Cancer survival comes in as many shades as people are different. Pick out the information that works for you and ignore the rest. At this time, put yourself first. You will find your values change and priorities shift and somehow you come out a stronger, more caring person. ~ Bea Vining

Don't time travel. Stick to getting through one day at a time rather than looking too far ahead. ~ Valorie Steichen

My funniest moment was when I was at my son's basketball game, and I had just been diagnosed with my cancer. A lady I know in the stands called out to me as I walked by, "Mara, did you find out the results of your tests? Do you have breast cancer?" I felt humiliated for a split second but after glancing around, I noticed all the looks of concern so I said, "Yes," and continued walking to my seat. We laugh about it today! ~ Mara Solberg

I had just been diagnosed and was standing out in my yard when my neighbor guy yelled, "You buy your plot yet?" I could not believe he just said that, but I yelled back, "NO!" I'm not going to die from this. I'm a survivor. ~ Lisa Verworn

One thing is certain after you receive your diagnosis: you look at the future through a different lens. It's a lens of new priorities that put family, friends, and those you hold dear first. You are humbled by the rally that occurs around you and inspired by amazing stories from survivors. ~ Judy Green

nice pair.
(bosc pears, acacia flowers, monkey tail fern, earrings, button & painted stones)

FEAR

Most days, fear is less and hope is more. Laughter comes more easily some days, tears on others. Some days are deluged with both. Just the way they were "before." ~ Margaret Unruh

It wasn't until a group of survivors met with me that I learned that thinking nonstop about the cancer—even at 3:00 a.m.—was a normal response: I wasn't going crazy!! I was very lucky to have so many long-term friends and a close family—even though many couldn't express their thoughts appropriately to someone who was going through cancer! ~ Bea Vining

Eventually, the loneliness of my initial internal monologue of fear and doubt silences and gives way to dialogue: productive and fruitful and life-driven. Increasingly along this journey, I realize that each day brings a "start-over"—that blank backdrop for the colors of today: a new day. Suddenly, melting the bangs of my wig seems so insignificant. ~ Margaret Unruh

Diversion from the cancer is hard to come by. Find one thing that puts you in your best mood and use it the days you're overwhelmed by the cancer. Massages, movies, etc. Mine was lunch with friends. A friend, also a survivor, labeled it our WHINE and cheese sessions. There is also one rule: we have to laugh—and you know what? It works!! ~ Bea Vining

cabranet.

(wine glasses, cabernet sauvignon wine, cork, grapevines & unripened red grapes)

It is okay to put myself first sometimes. And it's okay to accept help from others. Focusing on getting me healthy was now the priority. It is tough news for your friends and family to take, but by letting them help out in any way possible, they feel better, too. Accept their help! ~ Kelsey Christian

I understand how important it is to love like crazy and freely forgive. ~ Kelsey Christian

brawberry fruit tart.
(tarts, custard, kiwi, strawberries, blueberries, blackberry & creeping jenny leaves)

SURGERY

My siblings are not nurses, but one works at a clinic so, by default, she became qualified to remove my surgical dressings—the ones the surgeon says you can take off at home. I had two breasts in those spots less than 48 hours ago and you want me to what??? She said it looked like I had two really bad sprained ankles. (She lied.) We found ourselves giggling, though, and I wished so much she had not needed to do this—and thanked God that she could. ~ Margaret Unruh

Choosing to have a bilateral mastectomy at 25 was a no-brainer. Being identified as a carrier for the BRCA 1 cancer gene and losing so many women in my family to cancer with half their lives left, I knew I didn't want to spend the greater part of my life fearing, "What if today is the day I wake up and everything changes?" I choose to focus on everything I have to live for and not what I have lost. ~ Samantha Meyer

Bending over to retrieve my bag of candy at the check-out line at the grocery store, I found myself eye to eye with a little girl. Her eyes grew very large with her little hand covering her mouth in a gesture of surprise. The words she uttered were priceless and straightforward. "Lady, you lost your boobers." I realized very quickly that by bending over, this child was given a glimpse of my scarred chest, booberless and all. "Yes sweetie, I had surgery." "Oh my!" she gasped and then recovered quickly. "My dad got a bad I N F E C T I O N in his finger once and the doctor lopped it off. Did they lop your boobers off?" It was then that her mother overheard, embracing a can of vegetables and catching the end of our conversation. To say she was mortified would be indubitably an understatement. She told me that her daughter can be quite precocious and asked her to apologize to me. I could see the gears agitating in her little head. Finally she blurted, "I am sorry your boobers were lopped off." The expression on her mother's face could not be replicated in a million years; it was sheer exasperation. I was a privileged participant in this timeless moment. I hoped she would not be scolded terribly for her honest comments. For, she was very right...I lost my boobers. ~ Kim Wagner

Because of breast cancer, I value my faith, family & friendships more deeply. I recognized after my double mastectomy that one's body and other superficial images don't represent who we are. It's not the external—but the internal—that matters most. ~ Mari Bindas

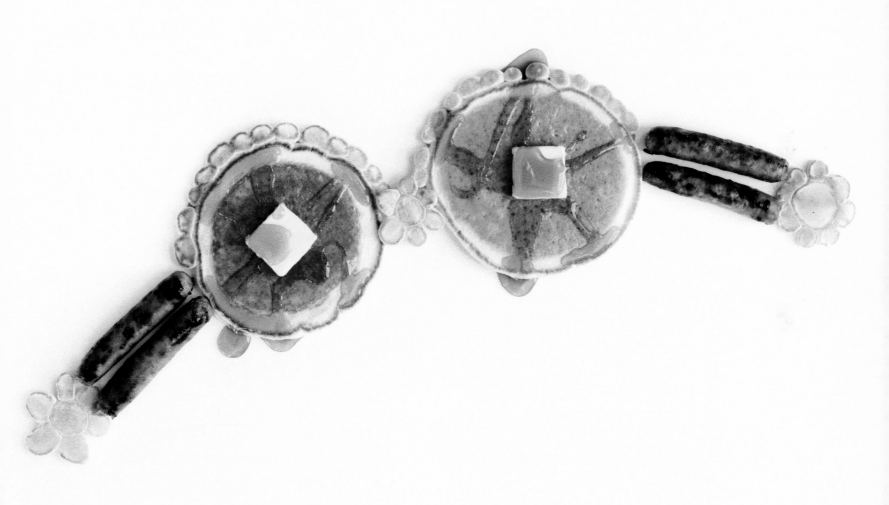

flat as a pancake.
(pancakes, sausages, butter & maple syrup)

I had just gotten out of the shower at my local gym and was putting lotion on before I got dressed. It was early morning on a weekend, and I had the locker room to myself. Suddenly, I heard the door to the locker room open. Panicked, I immediately thought to myself, "Quick!! Grab a towel!!" In frenzy, I dropped my lotion, grabbed a towel, and quickly wrapped it around my body at lightning-fast speed. I remember feeling a little resentful that I no longer felt confident with my unclothed body. Cancer is so unfair that way! So, it struck me as incredibly funny that morning when I heard the shuffle of footsteps near me, peered over my shoulder, and I looked up just in time to see...a blind lady and her assistance dog! I started laughing as I realized the irony of it. None of us have perfect bodies, and I need to be thankful for what I have. Cancer may have stolen my breasts, but all of my other body parts are intact. I might have saggy skin from losing weight, but I'm lean and I know the joy of being an endurance athlete. I'm still alive, and so is my mind, my spirit, and my determination. I had never seen that blind lady in the locker room until that morning, and I haven't seen her since. I think she may have been an angel...~ Lori Ellingson

One evening, I found myself running outside to our hot tub topless, thinking to myself that I can get away with it! After all, I am boobless and bald. Anyone who sees me in here will think I'm a guy! The thought literally left me laughing out loud! At that moment I thanked God for warming my heart with the gift of humor and laughter! It was medicine to my soul! ~ Mari Bindas

The gift of humor is surely a grace to get you through! ~ Mari Bindas

flasher.

(vintage flash attachments, flash bulbs, lens hood, shutter cables, 35mm b/w film, magnifying filter & view finder)

My youngest grandson, who was three at the time, would sit on my lap and be affectionate. Before he'd get on my lap he'd say, "Grandma is that your 'owie' side?" He'd proceed up on my lap making sure he didn't bump my bad side. One morning while sitting on my lap, he looked at me so lovingly and said, "Grandma, I just love your wrinkle." He pointed to a wrinkle at my eye that he saw as I sat smiling at him. He was so compassionate while expressing his love; it was so sincere. ~ Rachel Bearfield

I run a daycare and, after my lumpectomy, the smaller children, who loved to be held and snuggled, noticed that one breast was different and they kept patting the one that had changed. So the children moved to the more familiar side and were happy and everything was great again. ~ Sue Brown

My cancer treatment involved the removal of a lump above my right nipple. The surgeon did a marvelous job, and the only thing I noticed after healing was a slight reduction in the size of that breast. Over time however, age, loss of muscle mass, and weight gain started to have an effect on my body. One morning I was standing in front of the bathroom mirror without anything on my top. My hands were overhead as I was drying my hair. As I looked in the mirror reflecting back at me was what I could only explain as a "high beam" right breast, paired with a "low beam" left breast. I was momentarily dismayed but then broke out in laughter at the thought of the out-of-sync headlights! ~ Amy Ruley

no lumps, thank you.

(teacups, saucers, spoons, tea ball, English ivy, sweet broom genista, sugar tongs & sugar cubes)

RECONSTRUCTION

When I was diagnosed, my parents were telling my younger brother (11 at the time) that I was having surgery, but that I would be able to put something in my bra to make it look more normal. He then asked, "Like what, coconuts?" When I began reconstruction, he asked me if I had my coconuts put in! ~ Alishia Daily

A friend of mine spent her summers working in the lingerie department. A lady who had undergone a mastectomy of her left breast followed by reconstruction was being fitted; she stated that the tissue used to create a new breast also had created a problem. It seemed the replacement tissue used was from the stomach area. Now, the lady said, whenever she gained weight, her left breast was the body part that became bigger and bigger. ~ Gloria Anderson

While discussing reconstruction with my surgeon, I realized I don't have to stick with what nature gave me...so why not show the girls some love and go a little bigger! ~ Samantha Meyer

After a bilateral mastectomy as a BRCA 1 carrier, my friends tease me that when we're 80 and in the nursing home together, I'll be the one sitting in a bikini top with my perky breasts. ~ Beth Meyer

implants.
(echevaria, rumpus grass, hens & chicks, iris leaves, dusty miller, soil & stone)

ENHANCERS

For awhile, my clothing, and especially a favorite black top, kept turning on my body. I didn't think much about it, but was mildly annoyed as I kept turning it back to center. One day, out of the blue it dawned on me…I was no longer symmetrical. I was no longer a two-fer. I became a one and a half-er. I had tried a certain bra with a cotton insert. The insert did not want to stay in place and kept coming to the front, so I became a three-fer; with a rightie, a leftie, and a center. ~ Carol Weiss

Not long after I went through my treatment, I got myself a puppy. I had always wanted one, and now I had a perfectly good reason to give myself a "present." One early morning, I could hear my puppy chewing on something on the floor. What could it be? I looked over and couldn't really see anything, so I rolled over and went back to sleep. But I kept waking up, worrying about what he was chewing on, so I decided I had better know. I got up, and lo and behold, he was chewing on and eating my breast prosthesis. Oh no, now I had two problems. I had to go to work and I had no prosthesis, and was my puppy going to get sick? ~ Violet Deilke

My decision to pursue breast reconstruction finalized one sunny summer day. Picture a lake full of people. I jumped off the end of the dock, came up from the water to find one of my prosthetics floating on top of the water!!! My first thought was, "Thank goodness it didn't sink! Those things are expensive!" ~ Cindy Wateland

My first swimming experience with my prosthetic was very interesting. I was on vacation with my husband and kids. Prior to the vacation, I had checked into buying a new swimsuit with the wonderful breast prosthetic pockets. The swimsuits were pretty spendy, and I had a perfectly good suit, so I figured I would not spend the money on a "special" swimsuit. I remember telling my husband these suits were a big gimmick and people didn't really need them. So I walked into the pool area all smug and came to the edge of the pool and dove in. Seconds after hitting the water, I realized something was not right. I emerged my head from the water—and calmly tried to inform my husband I had a problem: my prosthetic did not stay where it should have! It was nestled nicely in the crotch of my suit! I was in complete shock. Slowly I maneuvered myself closer to my husband. I slowly moved the prosthetic up and out by my armpit while keeping my body, with the exception of my head, under water. My husband then leaned close, cupped his hands around the prosthetic and held it close to his body, concealing every inch of it. He walked swiftly to the shelves of towels and grabbed one. He wrapped it up tightly and handed it to me. I was still pondering how to get out of the pool without notice. I climbed up the ladder, placed my right hand over my left chest area and grabbed my towel to quickly cover up. I rushed to the room to readjust and catch my breath from hysterically laughing about the situation. I did return to the pool but, needless to say, I did not go back in the water. In fact, I did not go back into a pool until after I had a new swimsuit—with the wonderful prosthetic pockets. ~ Theresa Larson

nest enhancement.
(bird nests, dried monkey tail fern, bacopa, pebbles, beach glass, ribbon & parakeet feathers)

CHEMOTHERAPY

A friend I hadn't seen in years found out my worst day of chemo was each Wednesday and marked it on her calendar so that a card arrived every week on Wednesday. She will never know how much that meant! I started looking forward to the mail, and it turned the day around. It gave me something to look forward to. I knew I could never repay her, but I've tried to remember the little things you can do for people are very important. My husband and I then tried to plan something special for the week after chemo. I found it was a distraction, something to talk about and plan for. Things like a small get-away...perhaps to a movie or new restaurant. It kept us focused on something positive and fun in the future. ~ Cari Wefel

As my body struggles to adjust to toxins that sometimes bring hours and even whole days to a halt, I have learned to allow my heart and mind time to "wander around."

There comes the opportunity, the necessity, to stop and to patiently focus on the bigger picture...to "shhh." To be quiet. ~ Margaret Unruh

A neighbor said, "Lisa, I didn't know you had a pacemaker." It was my port...~ Lisa Verworn

I never wore a wig or hat, but would occasionally wear a scarf for the parents at my daycare. The children thought my bald head was beautiful but needed their attention through repeated application of hand lotion; I loved them helping me through this with their warm little hands and hearts. ~ Sue Brown

On the last day of chemo, we all had a "happy day dance."
~ Marlys Martin

pecs of steel.
(copper wire, knives, lock, bolt, washers, aluminum & steel)

CHEMOBRAIN

Under the influence of chemo, I made 8.5 x 11 Christmas cards using a picture of myself when I was bald. The cards were HUGE, and I had no idea I had done this until I went to pick them up and was told, "Your total is $96.00 ma'am." I almost fainted and explained my chemobrain situation. They just said, "No problem," threw them out, and allowed me to start over. ~ Lisa Verworn

The first time I had a major "chemobrain" incident, I was driving. I had read that some people got lost; I suddenly didn't have a clue where I was going, how I got where I was, or where to go from there. I got the giggles and that turned into royal laughter, and I kept on driving. After all, I was in Fargo...if I just kept on going I was eventually going to get to somewhere I was familiar with. I ended up getting a coffee and finding my way home. I have no idea if that was my original plan or not, but any fears I had were turned into a sense of adventure, laced with a hearty dose of laughter therapy. I have never been afraid of chemobrain since. Actually, "chemobrain" is a very handy tool for a random person, and it has given me many hearty laughs. ~ Carol Weiss

training bra.
(training wheels, bicycle chain & bell)

FRIENDS

The best things that were done for me were cards, calls, and prayers from people who I didn't really know all that well. I read those cards so many times throughout that year and they made me feel so good. So that is what I try to do for someone when I hear they have been diagnosed with some form of cancer. I call, send a card, or take them to a treatment because I know what those small gestures of kindness meant to me. I guess they call it "paying it forward." ~ Vickie Kelly

A few of my closest friends put together a big care basket for me, complete with a homemade blanket and chemo cap, baby shampoo for my peach fuzz hair, magazines, protein shakes, ginger ale, and pink ribbon bracelets; they each had one, too! There was a homemade coupon book with coupons for things like a free meal, a free back rub, a free shoulder to cry on, and even coupons for me to use their notes when I had to miss class! ~ Alishia Daily

A very dear and concerned friend asked how I was feeling while I was undergoing chemotherapy. I responded by telling her how very exhausted chemotherapy was making me. Good intentioned, but under informed, she proceeded to ask me why I didn't just drink more coffee to offset the chemotherapy side effects. Yes...if it were only that simple. It's at that point I realized this is just one of those things people truly don't understand until they themselves have lived it. ~ Heather DeBoer

When I was diagnosed with cancer and had finished up chemo and was completely bald, my friends and I took a trip to a local supermarket. We were in the hair products aisle and my friend looked at me and asked, "Have you tried the new root booster that they got at the salon?" I looked at her with a puzzled look and said, "No, can't say that I have." She then said, "You should—it works great!" With that, she proceeded down the aisle. I found my other friend and started to tell her the story when we heard her let out an, "OH MY GOSH!" It had just hit what she had said to me. We still laugh at that story! ~ Pam Knapper

I could never say that I am glad to have had breast cancer, but my life is so much better since my diagnosis. I have found a set of SASSY SURVIVOR friends who are remarkable. We laugh and cry—and do a lot of shopping together! ~ Cindy Wateland

breast-buds.
(depression glass flower frogs, sweetheart rosebuds, ferns, vintage lace,
ribbon, heart, green trick dianthus, string & buttons)

SPOUSES

Food is food, and my husband is here to stay. I'm thankful for a husband who will ask what I want to eat, patiently stop cooking it when it smells gross, finish cooking it when all is well—only to have me look at whatever "it" is and say, "I'm sorry. I can't eat that." ~ Margaret Unruh

My husband listens to my same worries over and over, rubs my feet, and accepts that sometimes leftover lasagna IS breakfast. Convinced beyond all measure that I will get better, he is dedicated to his promise to keep reminding me of this if (and when) I get discouraged. As we've always said, after nearly 5, 10, 15, 20, 25, 30 years: we have way too much invested in this relationship to give up now. ~ Margaret Unruh

covering second base.
(vintage baseball gloves, baseball, peanuts & Cracker Jacks with prizes)

After 25 years of marriage, there is no doubt diagnosis brought greater depth to our relationship. My husband has been my champion throughout my professional journey. Now, he has become my champion in this personal journey. He has been a rock by sharing his support tenfold. Right after the diagnosis, he had a strong need to rally. He responded to this need by surprising many family and friends with pink bracelets he ordered online. They stated: CANCER SUCKS. People responded with smiles and laughter, and immediately put the bracelet on their wrist. They were worn by many every day throughout my journey. It was awesome. ~ Judy Green

My husband is what one would call a man's man. But he really stepped up to the plate. Following my surgery, I was told not to lift my arms over my head. That can make it rather difficult to do anything with your hair. I wasn't even sure my husband knew what a curling iron was, let alone how to use one. Well, he proved me wrong. I went back to work three weeks following surgery, and I wasn't going without having my hair looking somewhat presentable; he was not going to let me disobey "doctor's orders." So he curled my hair for me. He only burned my forehead and neck once. And, I must say, my hair looked good. ~ Mary Sprague

nice rack.
(deer antler sheds, wool felted balls,
vintage brooch & leather belt)

FAMILY

Our family has realized just how precious our time together is. We don't spend nearly as much time worrying about things that don't matter, but more time just doing the things that we love to do with each other. ~ Valorie Steichen

My wig was a source of entertainment on a variety of occasions. We had a gathering of our women's basketball team at my home over the holidays; they truly became an extended part of my family. I had gone to use the restroom and, for some reason, decided it would be fun to see what I might look like if I put my wig on backwards. I turned it around and, while gazing in the mirror, found the look to be hilarious. So I casually walked back into the room, and the entire group broke out in laughter. We then decided it would be amusing to see what each and every person would look like in the wig. We took pictures of everyone sporting the new look. It was fun entertainment! ~ Amy Ruley

I believe the single most positive thing that has come from my cancer diagnosis is that my family (both blood relatives as well as friends) has become my #1 priority—always! There will always be time for work, cleaning, etc. But, when special events happen or your family/friends need you...you can't put them off or you will miss out on the joys in life! The entire journey has allowed me to completely refocus my life. ~ Denae Grove

Seeking some control...a clear way for me to demonstrate a little control during this journey was to plan Christmas photos in April. After surgery and before chemo, I decided it was time for this year's Christmas photo. Our son got engaged on Valentine's Day, so I wanted to be sure our card included his fiancée and also me with a full head of hair. It was a great family day for all of us. Everyone wore PINK for the photo, even our dog! ~ Judy Green

Snuggling on the couch watching a movie with my family as popcorn is innocently getting deposited into the carpet and couch by my young children; reading a library book to my children when dirty dishes are covering the countertops in the kitchen; sitting outside in the lawn watching my children explore and enjoy the outdoors even though the toilets need cleaning, floors need scrubbing, laundry needs doing...these are just a few of the events which happen regularly now, but didn't happen before my cancer diagnosis. ~ Heather DeBoer

deck the halls with bras of holly.
bra-la-la-la-la bra-la-la-la.
(pomegranates, cranberries, juniper, holly, birch bark & pinecone)

KIDS

On one particularly busy evening at the local café, my grandson was getting a little impatient to get his food, and he was very "active." Suddenly he decided I shouldn't be wearing my hat, so he reached up and pulled it off. Of course I quickly pulled it back on. He was so surprised to see me bald. He was very quiet the rest of the evening. ~ Donna Kratz

The children had a lot of questions, and many of them were tough to answer. One of the boys insisted upon knowing the statistics of my chances for survival, although he framed the question in terms of death versus survival. Some of the questions were downright comical, as when my five year-old asked me, "Mommy, when they cut off your breast, it will grow back, won't it?" ~ Cynthia Mohr

One evening we stopped at a fast-food restaurant's drive-through for our supper. Upon returning home, my eight year-old daughter asked where the straws were for our shakes. I told her that they were not in the bag and we would have to go with a different plan. She quickly replied, "If you would have told them you have cancer, they would have given you straws." ~ Katy Koehn

My niece asked me to speak about breast cancer awareness and to share my cancer journey at her school's assembly. Throughout the month, children in grades K-12 jotted down messages of encouragement for me and collected them in a plastic pumpkin. After speaking that day, I was sent home with dozens of sweet notes, such as:

"I hope you get better cause I feal so bad. I feal really really really really really really bad. Not just a little, but really bad."

"My pray's are alway's with you. Be carful!"

"I am sorry that you have bress canser. I wish you wod fel better."

"I think it is so sad to have cancer. My grandpa had cancer and all I would like to say to you is...good luck."

"I hope u get better so u can be a nice lady because u seem like a nice person. I want u to be my frend. Get super super super well soon."

Whenever I was having a difficult day, I'd pull out a note from the pumpkin and find myself smiling! ~ Kim Wagner

sweet puppies.
(Chihuahua puppies, leashes, ball & dog treat)

Throughout my breast cancer journey, I have discovered one thing: this isn't the club I ever dreamed of joining; however, there are a LOT of amazing people who are members.

~ Denae Grove

BALD & BEAUTIFUL

A friend had a hat shower for me after I lost my hair. It was a fun evening full of lots of laughter as I opened each gift and tried on the hats. We had pink ribbon decorations on the treats that she served, too. It was something that made me feel very cared for. ~ Becky Heinsen

Shaving my head was better than mourning the loss of my hair. Seeing the hair on my pillow, in the sink and shower, and worrying about it "blowing away in the wind" was too much. I looked healthier without hair than I did with tufts! (And less scary to my kids!) ~ Kelsey Christian

When I started to lose my hair, I called up a good friend and asked that she come over for a visit and to bring her clippers. She arrived with tears in her eyes and said, "I don't think I can do this." "Oh, yes you can," I told her, "I've always wanted a Mohawk!" And that's what we did. I had wigs and scarves to cover it, but I had a very nice short Mohawk. We laughed until we cried. ~ Lori Boehmlehner

Whenever my head itched, I would take my wig and move it back and forth to scratch my head, embarrassing my husband. ~ Teri Gorze

I shared the idea for my "Art Hats" project with local Designing Quilters and the Fiber Guild groups. After all, the majority of women with breast cancer will lose their hair and need a hat or two. These creative individuals LOVED the idea and got very excited about the project. It seemed every time I needed encouragement, a hat would arrive in the mail or be given in person. Presently I have over 50 creative hats in "The sheARTS Project: Art Hats for Breast Cancer Awareness" collection—all hand-made by amazing supporters. ~ Claudia M. Pratt

When your hair is coming back and growing in dark and curly, don't tell your good friend who has dark and curly hair that you hate your "new" hair—because it is so dark and curly! ~ Abby Schmidt

brrrassiere.
(snowballs, carrots, scarf & buttons)

WIGS

I felt better when I kept busy, so I spent many days baking pies and giving them to people I cared about. When money became a problem, I began to sell pies to friends and family to pay for gas. When I went to see my hairstylist for a wig, I was able to pay for one with pie money! ~ Mara Solberg

I even played the "cancer card" by taking "Julia" (my wig) off when a sheriff stopped by our lake to inquire about a boat license number. I thought, "Who is going to give a poor chemotherapy patient a fine?" ~ Julie Larson

One of the most anxious moments came when I went in to get my head shaved. After my hairstylist shaved it, both she and my husband commented that I had a really nice shaped head—no funny bones or blemishes on it. When she put the wig on, I thought, "This is the best my hair has ever looked." Other gals had asked if I could come with them to their hairstylist to get their hair cut like my wig. I said, "Well the beauty of this wig is that I don't even have to come with you. You can just bring the wig!" ~ Julie Larson

It had been a couple of months since my final chemo treatment, and my hair was just beginning to grow back. We were having basketball practice in the excessively warm gym this particular day. I was becoming very warm and found the wig to be itchy and irritating. The women on the team encouraged me to take it off. They said it wouldn't bother them, even though I had very little hair. So I decided to go ahead and remove it. I laid it on the stage at the north end of the floor. We were doing some drill work when our student trainer entered the gym. He walked toward the stage. Suddenly he jumped back in fear as he came upon the wig, which he thought was some type of rodent or animal. The girls on the team caught his reaction and burst out in laughter. He was quite relieved to find that it was not a living animal. ~ Amy Ruley

I kept a journal throughout my treatment, and I found it very cathartic to write in it. This particular entry was about the first time I washed my wig, which I affectionately named "Raquel." Raquel immediately lost her haughtiness and became, well, almost a wet-looking rodent. Some color came out in the water, which I hoped was normal, so I refrained from hyperventilating. Swish, swish and...WHAT WAS THAT??? I saw at least THREE stray hairs in the water, no longer attached. Cha-ching! I couldn't help but think, "Oh, $25 here or $25 there and it's NOT growing back!" One more cycle of washing and rinsing and we were done. Next came the process of lightly combing her out, from the bottom up. A couple more hairs came out. %$*&^!! You know how some people use the excuse that they have to stay home because they have to wash their hair? Well, this brings new meaning to an old excuse. ~ Krystal Anderson

sports bra.

(soccer ball, volleyball, softball, golf balls, golf tees, tennis arm bands, neoprene knee braces & ponytail elastic)

Like most women who lose their hair during chemotherapy treatment, I struggled with the decision about whether to wear a wig or a scarf. I finally decided that I would wear a wig. I named my wig "Pippi" because Pippi Longstocking was a beloved character from a favorite childhood book— and because the name seemed "sassy" and "plucky," just how I hoped to be as I experienced my new life as a breast cancer survivor. Pippi helped me feel comfortable during the day as an elementary teacher; however, I couldn't wait to put her on her little Styrofoam head the moment I walked in the house in exchange for a knit cap. One of my favorite caps was my pink "house turban." When I paired my pink "house turban" with a nice pair of dangly earrings, I actually looked a little like a French painter. I considered setting up an easel near the front door so if anyone stopped by, they would mistake me for a budding artist instead of a cancer patient. ~ Stephenie Herbranson

There I was, standing in the front, singing up a storm. I looked at my daughter, who was sitting in the front row. She proceeded to gesture to me, putting her hands up on each side of her head, pulling her hands down like she had a wig on. I didn't know my wig was coming off. It was sitting totally kittywampus. I turned around, threw my choral book, and pulled my wig down. Everybody had seen what was happening, and all I could do was shrug my shoulders and laugh. Needless to say, that was the end of the wig; I quickly became a constant "hat wearer," embellishing when I could. ~ Cindy Koziol

Christmas last year, my sisters decided to put makeup on my Styrofoam wig head, giving her the name "LuLu." While traveling to our grandparents' home, they set LuLu in the back window of our vehicle facing out, so that she could observe the cars behind us! ~ Alishia Daily

I had lots of fun with my wig since I didn't like wearing it. There was the day at work when I took it off and left it lying on my desk. My co-worker came around the corner into my office, stopped short, and said, "For a minute I thought you had a puppy on your desk!" ~ Becky Heinsen

When my hair was growing back, my kids could not believe how soft it was. It was as soft as the hair on a baby's head. I told them it felt like theirs did when they were little. The softness of my hair made it irresistible to leave alone. They were always running their fingers through it! ~ Kathy Skjervheim

perfect measurements.
(vintage tape measure, pliers, needle-nose pliers, screwdriver, bolt & string)

RADIATION

My last radiation treatment was on St. Patrick's Day, an easy date to remember. Although I wanted to celebrate, I must admit that my treatments were not a negative experience. The radiation therapy staff was terrific, and I was actually going to miss seeing them every day. Being someone who just loves a good joke, I felt I had to end the treatment journey with a laugh. As I prepared to go into the radiation treatment room, I placed a shamrock sticker on my breast. As the girls were positioning me for my treatment and moved my gown, they saw the shamrock and were shocked. Everyone had to come over and see it, and we laughed and laughed. ~ Betty Neubert

Having four adult children living in several states, I found the best way to converse with them was by e-mail: no preferential treatment. They all received the news at the same time. I updated them frequently on the treatments. I truly had no complaints, but they seemed to think I was sparing them from complaining about any adverse conditions. So after my twelfth radiation treatment, I decided to give them what they were waiting for. In the subject line of an e-mail, I wrote, "THEY DIDN'T SAY THIS WOULD HAPPEN!" That got their attention! In the body of the e-mail, I wrote, "Well, I had my twelfth radiation treatment today. I've been feeling well and haven't had any nausea, but there is one side effect that I don't remember anyone mentioning! I visited with my oncologist and brought up my concern. It turns out that the radiation not only evenly tans the 'bad breast,' but it also firms it, making it as 'perky' as it was when I was thirty! My concern is that the 'good breast' now just hangs there, like an almost 70-year-old breast, envious of the 'bad breast.' But alas, it turns out that my doctor said I could NOT get radiation to my 'good breast.'" ~ Marlene Ford

braw.

(sushi veggie roll, nigiri salmon, nigiri shrimp, salmon roe, sushi tuna roll, garlic chives, wasabi, carrot & shredded radish on rice paper)

SMALL BLESSINGS

The little things don't seem to matter much anymore. I had a friend come over to drive me somewhere after my surgery. She backed out of my garage...and broke off my mirror. She was so upset, and I was just like, "Who cares?!" and started laughing. ~ Abby Schmidt

Naps are a wonderful thing...if you need one, take one. ~ Valorie Steichen

I found so much inspiration through music; Laura Story's song "Blessings," in particular. "What if your blessings come through raindrops? What if your healing comes through tears?" My journey has led me back to my faith, and because of that, it has been my greatest blessing. ~ Michelle Forness

One thing I made a point of doing was always wearing makeup and dressing nicely. Often, I treated myself to a rose on the table. My advice: talk about how you feel and find someone to listen. ~ Barb Rudh

From my standpoint, the words of encouragement I received from my amazing doctor were things I held onto tightly. She said things like: "Of course you will swim with your grandchildren," and "Of course you will retire with your husband." There truly is an "upside" to cancer; I decided to retire early so I could spend more time with my husband. Learning to "de-stress" and take the time to do things I really enjoy—yes—we can make lemonade from the lemons of life! ~ MaDonna Stanford

I learned to laugh at myself...many times! I could have cried, but laughing felt better. My emotions were pretty delicate—and still are at times, but I chose to laugh... laugh at the mess the kids made while I slept, laugh at the burnt meal my non-cooking husband made, or laugh at my attempts at drawing on eyebrows. I kept telling myself it wouldn't last forever. ~ Kelsey Christian

There are many kind acts that are done on a daily basis. I want to be able to do something kind every day for someone in need of it. I appreciated each and every kind thing done for me while I was in need. ~ Valorie Steichen

some BIG tomatoes.
(tomatoes, rosemary, basil & tomato leaves)

HOT FLASHES

I started to wear my wig in the summer, and it was very hot. The chemo put me into menopause. Believe it or not, my hot flashes were so bad that I singlehandedly fogged up all the windows in a car. Talk about a hot mama! ~ Teri Gorze

My hot flashes were so unbelievably awful that my husband would continuously wake up in the middle of the night (with no covers on, of course) absolutely freezing. One night he decided he had the perfect solution: he crawled into bed...and got into his sleeping bag. There were no more sleepless nights—and he was toasty warm! Truth be told, that is how we slept until I was able to get them under control. Problem solved! ~ Pam Knapper

Hot Ta-Tas!
(Mexican bowls, green onions, cilantro, ancient sweets, jalapeno, habanero & sweet peppers)

SCREENING

Oh well, like my friend says, "If life gives you lemons...tuck 'em inside your bra! Couldn't hurt, might help!" ~ Marlene Ford

I have not always been an outgoing person; as a little girl, I was quite shy. But as I grew older, I started to enjoy meeting people—those I already knew and new people. It was an opportunity to help make their day better for having seen, met, and talked with me. I also felt that it was important for me to smile not only with my mouth, but also with my eyes. I still live my life like that now, but I also take every opportunity afforded me to talk with people—both women and men—about the importance of monthly self-breast exams, mammograms, annual physical exams, and just to know your own body. ~ Cindy Eggl

Each year I give myself a birthday gift: a physical and mammogram. ~ Barb Rudh

freshly squeezed.
(vintage juice reamer, lime squeezer, navel oranges, Key lime & Meyer lemon)

STRENGTH

For the past two years, my family and extended family have walked in the breast cancer walk on Mother's Day at the local mall. The first year I was in a wheelchair, which didn't make me happy. This past year it was a very rainy day, so I made it halfway. Next year my goal is to do the entire walk. ~ Marlys Martin

It's hard to believe how breast cancer can empower you. I never perceived myself as one who could overcome such adversity. ~ Diane Tangen

Shortly after I was diagnosed with breast cancer, a friend of mine began knitting a pink blanket for me. After she finished, she secretly invited our friends over to her house to help tie the fringe onto the blanket. As if this wasn't special enough, each of them brought a charm with them and they tied those charms into the fringe. They presented the blanket to me "ambush style," descending upon my house like women on a mission the weekend before my first round of chemo. I told my family members and friends how I had received such an awesome gift and soon others started sending charms to tie onto my blanket: charms reminding me of special times we shared, like ice cream cones and vacations; charms reminding me of my Irish heritage and family far away, like shamrocks and Celtic crosses. Some sent charms of my favorite things like Diet Mountain Dew and Hot Tamales. Charms of hope, courage, luck, and faith were all added to my blanket. I brought this blanket with me to every chemo treatment. Even though only three people could fit comfortably into the infusion rooms, I felt as though I had a whole team of support there as I wrapped that blanket around me. ~ Suzanne Darling

I had read from my breast cancer devotional about not being able to experience victory unless there was a battle. There were many days when I felt like I was in the midst of a fierce battle, a battle for my life. The cancer was the war, and getting through the treatment or the day was one of dozens of battles. ~ Cynthia Mohr

how the breast was won.

(Wyoming split heel spurs, leather spur straps, Colt 1849 revolver, Colt 1877
Lightening revolver, ivory poker chips, sheriff badge, bullets & buttons)

As a teacher, you need an objective for your lessons. Cancer taught me how to live. My parents had planned to go to Hawaii "after the kids were grown." My father died before that could happen. I knew I could not wait for what I wanted until I had accomplished everything for everybody else, so, since 2000, every two years I go to Europe. We make it happen. You may ask yourself, "How?" It is too expensive, takes too much time, my kids are too important to me, I can't leave my job…I asked myself, "Were those not the same concerns that you had when you were diagnosed with cancer?" I had to learn that opportunities open up if I look outside the boundaries I have accepted as normal. I ask myself, "What do I really want?" and don't focus on what is expected of me. Cancer taught me that when I decided to survive. ~ Marti Simmons

Each day is a gift. For years I heard this expression and now I know it and live it. ~ Diane Tangen

I think of my journey with cancer as kind of like that of having a baby. There were painful parts, days I don't want to remember, gross things that happened to my body, exhausting just-get-through-it moments. But in the end, all I remember are the good things: the people who loved me, helped me, cared for me. I recall the thoughtfulness and kindness of others and the feelings of strength and determination. I know I made it through this incredible journey and, granted, I don't have a beautiful bundle of joy to share, but at the end of it all, I have a sense of pride that I made it and came through it a better, stronger person. ~ Suzanne Darling

I have learned that life is uncertain. Don't waste time doing something you don't enjoy. Do those things you have thought about but haven't been brave enough to do. I have bravely changed the course of my life and ventured into starting a new business that I had dreamed about for a number of years. Make a bucket list of things you want to do—and actually do them—instead of just thinking about them. ~ Becky Heinsen

sea cup.

(fan coral, sea urchin, shell, sea biscuit, Mexican tile, snow crab claw, pearls, lock, stone, beach glass, doll arm, fishing line, lead weight, hook & wire).

HOPE

I had just started my new journey, the one I never planned for, never anticipated. This journey grabbed me out of my comfortable life into a nightmare that I couldn't escape. What I didn't know was that there was a story in northern Minnesota that was just unfolding: a story about two black bears whose journeys were about to coincide with mine. An organization in northern Minnesota had installed a camera in a black bear's den—a bear that was expected to have a cub in the coming days. Somehow, in the middle of the nightmare that I was living day by day, this bear brought such a smile to my face! In the middle of tears, fears, despair, anxiety, and uncertainty, this bear cub brought a new joy into my life. Little did they know, these bears became my companions on my cancer journey. At first, the baby (appropriately named "Hope") was hidden in her mother Lily's fur, but little by little she made her way out to where we could see her. I am thankful that I was able to have these beautiful animals be a part of my journey. We started our journey together and by the time I was heading back to work, the bears were leaving their den. At a time in my life when I felt that I would never get through another day without tears, they gave me glimpses of the joy—and so much "Hope" that I was afraid I would never experience again. ~ Judy Frasz

Two of my former co-workers delivered a huge smiley-faced flower balloon to me during a chemo session. It was so big I could not walk with it beside me, so I had to leave the cancer center with it floating over my head. I got lots of smiles and chuckles from people watching me walk out with the balloon, which made me (and everyone I encountered) feel much better, too. When we got outside to get in the vehicle, the wind was so strong we had to fight with it to get it into the car with us. That balloon kept me company for many weeks during chemotherapy. The balloon brought comfort and joy and was a token of hope! ~ Cindy Eggl

I was treated with chemotherapy, surgery, and radiation for my cancer. At the time, I truly believed I knew the meaning of the word compassion. Looking back, I was wrong. Now I do. Until one has gone through cancer, it's tough to grasp the concept. It's having a deep awareness of the suffering of others. Before going through cancer, when I showed compassion, I was only skimming the top. I hope I have changed in that way. When I know someone has been diagnosed, I call, write notes, send books, a journal, or food. Those are the things I really appreciated. ~ Marietta Weber

yup, they're reel.
(Bakelite handle fishing reels, fishing rod, cork bobber, vintage fishing lures & flies)

I was diagnosed when I was 24 years old. No family history, no significant health history. I never in a million years thought I'd get breast cancer. Obviously, I wish I had never gotten breast cancer; however, I feel that I am a stronger person for what I've gone through. I feel that there is a reason I was diagnosed, even though I don't know it yet, and that reason may be to be a resource for other young women. If this was going to happen to anyone in my family, it might as well be me. I could use my battle with breast cancer as an example and be a resource for other young women. ~ Alishia Daily

I could probably come up with a list of well over a hundred nice things people did for me and my family during that time in our lives. Some of these people were friends, some were family and some were even total strangers, but all of these people gave pieces that assembled the tow rope, which eventually pulled us from the ditch cancer threw us in. For a mother, one of the most heart-wrenching experiences is knowing that your child has a need and then coming to the realization that you can't meet that need

for them. Immediately, friends and relatives stepped up to the plate and nurtured and cared for my children during the times when I could not. Because they were so giving and selfless, my children have been able to experience many days with many different and amazing people. These people played a part in helping my children constructively process and adapt to the fact that mommy has cancer and life is different but it will be okay. As a mom, anyone who loves your child like that holds a very special place in your heart. ~ Heather DeBoer

Accept from others willing and wanting to do something for you. One day you will feel well enough to return the favor, and it feels great to be able to do so. ~ Valorie Steichen

Helping other women and knowing that I have possibly made another woman's journey easier by sharing my story has added the most meaning to my life. ~ Lisa Verworn

yup, they're reel.
(Bakelite handle fishing reels, fishing rod, cork bobber, vintage fishing lures & flies)

I was diagnosed when I was 24 years old. No family history, no significant health history. I never in a million years thought I'd get breast cancer. Obviously, I wish I had never gotten breast cancer; however, I feel that I am a stronger person for what I've gone through. I feel that there is a reason I was diagnosed, even though I don't know it yet, and that reason may be to be a resource for other young women. If this was going to happen to anyone in my family, it might as well be me. I could use my battle with breast cancer as an example and be a resource for other young women. ~ Alishia Daily

I could probably come up with a list of well over a hundred nice things people did for me and my family during that time in our lives. Some of these people were friends, some were family and some were even total strangers, but all of these people gave pieces that assembled the tow rope, which eventually pulled us from the ditch cancer threw us in. For a mother, one of the most heart-wrenching experiences is knowing that your child has a need and then coming to the realization that you can't meet that need

for them. Immediately, friends and relatives stepped up to the plate and nurtured and cared for my children during the times when I could not. Because they were so giving and selfless, my children have been able to experience many days with many different and amazing people. These people played a part in helping my children constructively process and adapt to the fact that mommy has cancer and life is different but it will be okay. As a mom, anyone who loves your child like that holds a very special place in your heart. ~ Heather DeBoer

Accept from others willing and wanting to do something for you. One day you will feel well enough to return the favor, and it feels great to be able to do so. ~ Valorie Steichen

Helping other women and knowing that I have possibly made another woman's journey easier by sharing my story has added the most meaning to my life. ~ Lisa Verworn

shakers.

(maracas, woven headbands, silver earrings, wool brooch, beaded chokers)

Many things have changed in my life since I had cancer. I find myself wondering, "What will I do if it returns?" That question has a different answer every time I think about it. My husband, the love of my life, says, "It's a bump in the road." I'd like to think that my life and the lives of my kids and husband would forever be positively changed because of this. To be mad or angry forever is a tough way to live one's life. ~ Katy Koehn

I now know that life could change in a second, and so I try to live life to the fullest. I've promised myself to do at least one new thing a year. I never want to be lying on the couch thinking I'm going to die, saying to myself, "I wish I would have done…" ~ Lisa Verworn

My doctor says that I am in "partial-remission" for stage IV breast cancer. If I've learned anything, it's that life has no guarantees. I celebrated my 50th birthday in February 2012, and since I never married, I threw myself a BIG combination birthday bash/wedding dance. It was celebratory with three bands, great food, and lots of friends and family. It also was a successful fundraiser for "The Art-Heals Fund," which will award grants to nonprofits working with artists and art therapy projects. I've used art to help me throughout my own cancer journey and want others to have the ability to experience that when they are going through a life challenge. ~ Claudia M. Pratt

The positive side of the whole journey is that we experienced love all around us from many people through words, acts of kindness, prayer, etc.… We are different people because of the experience. I cannot say I would have accepted the challenge given the choice, but I am glad for the outcome of our lives—living with the good and the bad, because it makes us who we are today. ~ Kathy Skjervheim

I have been SO BLESSED, and SO LOVED! ~ Marlene Ford

Everything happens for a reason. We do not choose these types of situations but we do learn from them—and hopefully laugh from them—and above all, know that, because of them, we become who we are today." ~ Theresa Larson

melons.
(cantaloupe, watermelon & honeydew)

At some point the cancer may decide it wants to take over my body and destroy it in the process. However, my soul is not done with it yet, so the cancer will have to share. And for that I am grateful. ~ Joyce Ertelt

fully blossomed.
(peonies, spirea & lemon grass)

GRATITUDE

Our culture is so limited in its definition of wealth. We look at possessions and money to define our wealth. By that standard I have too many things and just enough money. However, I am an extremely wealthy woman. I am wealthy in friends. Psychologists say if a person has one close friend—bosom buddy, soul mate, BFF—in their life, they are fortunate and among the few. Friends know your heart and soul and love you anyway; give up their time and agenda when you have a need; they are there for you, always— with or without hair. I have at least a dozen of these girlfriends, and I am in awe of how sweetly—and completely—they love me. I am wealthy in the creative arts. I have friends and family who are musicians, artists, poets, and my life is so rich because of them. My home is filled with original works of art by family; sweet music, from jazz to praise and worship to classical, fills my home. I am wealthy in health. It is a dichotomy that I have had cancer twice, but I am a very healthy person in spite of that. My body is strong, and I choose to be an optimist. When I stop to count my blessings, the list goes on and on. I consider myself to be the wealthiest woman in town. ~ Carol Weiss

bountiful.
(gourds, vines, corn broom, wheat, thistle, pheasant feather, berzilia, pinecones, paper, birch bark & allium)

Sanford Health is the largest rural, not-for-profit health care system in the nation, with locations in 126 communities, in seven states. In addition, Sanford Health is developing international clinics in Ireland, Ghana, Israel, and Mexico.

Edith Sanford Breast Cancer, a Sanford Health initiative, is pioneering a bold new comprehensive approach to breast cancer screening, treatment, and research. Its mission is to unlock each woman's genetic code, advance today's prevention and treatment, and end breast cancer for future generations. The launch of this movement began with a gift from T. Denny Sanford, who tragically lost his mother, Edith, to breast cancer when he was just four years old.

embrace, Sanford Health's Cancer Survivorship Program, is dedicated to improving the quality of life of cancer patients. Throughout their journey, *embrace* connects survivors to resources and support, educates them about managing side effects, and empowers them to make positive changes in their life.

SANF⊖RD®
HEALTH

Edith Sanford™
BREAST CANCER

embrace.sanfordhealth.org

sanfordhealth.org

edithsanford.org

Sanford Health is the largest rural, not-for-profit health care system in the nation, with locations in 126 communities, in seven states. In addition, Sanford Health is developing international clinics in Ireland, Ghana, Israel, and Mexico.

Edith Sanford Breast Cancer, a Sanford Health initiative, is pioneering a bold new comprehensive approach to breast cancer screening, treatment, and research. Its mission is to unlock each woman's genetic code, advance today's prevention and treatment, and end breast cancer for future generations. The launch of this movement began with a gift from T. Denny Sanford, who tragically lost his mother, Edith, to breast cancer when he was just four years old.

embrace, Sanford Health's Cancer Survivorship Program, is dedicated to improving the quality of life of cancer patients. Throughout their journey, *embrace* connects survivors to resources and support, educates them about managing side effects, and empowers them to make positive changes in their life.

embrace.sanfordhealth.org

SANFØRD
HEALTH

sanfordhealth.org

edithsanford.org

bountiful.

(gourds, vines, corn broom, wheat, thistle, pheasant feather, berzilia, pinecones, paper, birch bark & allium)

MEG SPIELMAN PELDO, artist

Meg Spielman Peldo is a fine art & portrait photographer and ceramic artist whose work in both media has been featured on HGTV "That's Clever" artists series and can be found in private and corporate collections around the world. Her North Dakota images have been presented to dignitaries across Asia on multiple trade missions. Spielman has won numerous awards and licensed images with major publishers of greeting cards, calendars, and prints. The daughter of a lingerie designer for Hollywood Vassarette in the 1950s, she is happy to now be creating art bras. She lives in Fargo, North Dakota.

KIM WAGNER, interviewer

Kim Wagner has been writing and speaking professionally for over 15 years. She has inspired thousands of people to look at life as a series of celebrations, encouraging with spontaneity and humor. Diagnosed with Stage 3 breast cancer in June, 2011, Kim still sees herself as very blessed. She delivers life-changing messages at conferences, community events, parent and women's groups, and church gatherings. Kim is well-known for her entertaining, energetic and dynamic delivery. She is the wife to a Lutheran pastor, mother to four adult children and grandma to one grandson. The Wagners live in Fargo, North Dakota.

DR. SHELBY TERSTRIEP, medical oncologist

Dr. Shelby Terstriep is a medical oncologist at Sanford Health and has the honor of caring for breast cancer survivors each day. She is passionate about improving the quality of life throughout the cancer journey. She is the recipient of the American Cancer Society's prestigious Lane Adams quality of life award. She has the privilege of hearing first-hand the humorous stories and inspirational advice from amazing people, which inspired the creation of this book. She tries to use this advice to live a fuller and more meaningful life with her three children and amazing husband.

JENNA LINDER, survivorship coordinator

Jenna Linder is the coordinator of the embrace Cancer Survivorship Program at Sanford Health. She creates and organizes each of the events, programs, and services offered through the embrace program. She is truly the coordinator of all things detailed. She has the benefit of helping patients become connected, educated, and empowered throughout their cancer journey. Her grandfather was diagnosed with lung cancer in 2009 and lost his battle in 2011. Because of her personal experiences with cancer, she knows firsthand that there truly is healing in humor, which inspired and impassioned her work of coordinating the many details of this book. She and her husband, Justin, reside in Fargo, North Dakota.

thanks a bunch.

MANY HEARTFELT THANKS to Karen Stoker, owner of the artisan Hotel Donaldson, and her always dedicated and encouraging team (especially Alison & Maranda), for establishing "Bras on Broadway," the delightful, annual breast cancer fundraiser that inspired me to go down the path of creating my found object bras and this book; my husband, Greg Peldo, for your quirky witticisms and for believing in me; my kids, Maija and Jake & Ben Hendricks, for keeping me in the loop on a new generation of synonyms, your uplifting support, and legal counsel; friend Lisa Nichols, for your inspiration, humor, and from the heart feedback that I could always count on; Carol Spielman, for your fresh, outside the box perspectives and encouragement; Samantha Meyer, for your photography critiques, ideas, and adorable puppies; Kriss LeCocq, for your final tweaks on layout and design; Don Faulkner, for serendipitously bringing me that lovely, tiny bird nest that was too small and got my imagination spinning for the very first bra; Peter Erickson of Frontier Americana for trusting me with your intriguing collection of antique guns and western artifacts; Steve Johnson for always being there for opinions, framing, vintage dishes, whatever I need; Nora & Julia, for lending me your training wheels; all my great friends & family for digging out their fishing reels and maracas and boxing gloves and more...and for their never ending amusement, absurdity and one-liners; and you, Mom.